From the library of

Michael Dyson

Happy Birthday
1998

Love, always,

Mom & Dad

ROBERT AND OLIVER

ROBERT AND OLIVER

BILL PERRY

Illustrations by
XIANGYI MO

CollinsDove
An imprint of HarperCollins*Publishers*

A CollinsDove publication
An imprint of HarperCollins*Publishers* (Australia) Pty Ltd
(ACN 008 431 730)
22–24 Joseph Street
North Blackburn, Victoria 3130, Australia

First published 1994
This edition published 1995
Designed by Pier Vido
Cover design by Pier Vido
Cover illustration by Xiangyi Mo
Illustrations by Xiangyi Mo
Typeset in Australia by HarperCollins*Publishers*, Melbourne
Printed in Hong Kong by HarperCollins*Publishers*

The National Library of Australia
Cataloguing-in-Publication Data:
Perry, Bill, 1933–
    Robert and Oliver.

ISBN 1 86371 486 3.

1. Cats — Fiction.   I. Title.

A823.3

The author's proceeds from sales of this book
will be donated to cancer research.

Contents

Preface

Within a few kilometres of Brisbane, in northern Australia, there is a house which, from its front, affords a clear view of the city and, at its rear, has a garden which merges into the bushland of Mt Coot-tha National Park. The garden, which is the home of Oliver, the old cat, and Robert, the young cat, is a special place.

On summer days iridescent blue butterflies provide colour points to overripe tropical greens. Brush turkeys strut the bounds of territories determined without reference to any surveyor's plan, and large lizards, the most common of which is the bearded dragon, resemble garden statues as they wait for the sun to warm the life force which will crack their suit of stone.

Evenings in the garden belong to the noisy possums, the silent owls and eerie fruit bats which pass through the tropic blackness in waves. Each dawn is heralded by the laugh of the kookaburra, and then by a rush of bird song, as each of the species strives to be first to respond to the signalling of a new day.

It is this special place which provides the setting for the stories of Robert and Oliver and those creatures with whom their lives intertwine.

Within a distance of Brisbane, so close that there is a temptation to reach out to touch the city lights, there is a garden, and it is within that garden, where the inhabitants seek not only to survive but to make sense of the purpose of being, that our stories find their stage.

Enter then, from left, right and above, Robert, the young cat, Oliver, the old cat, and, in turn, a companion cast of bushland creatures.

Now then, let the stories begin.

THERE IS A SEASON

Robert, the young cat, found Oliver, the old cat, nestled in the crisp brown leaves under a bottlebrush tree.

"What do you think about?" asked Robert.

"I think about tomorrow," replied Oliver.

"Why not come with me and chase sunbeams?" said Robert.

Oliver smiled a faint smile and said, "Thank you, Robert, but I prefer to dream. When I was young I chased sunbeams, but now I must try to understand the meaning of days gone by, by thinking of the days to come."

Robert was no longer listening, for his eyes were upon a bright green grasshopper and the chase was rising within him.

BLOWING BUBBLES

When the mood took them, Oliver, the old cat, and Robert, the young cat, would groom each other. As it is pleasant for humans to engage in convivial conversation, so it is for cats to participate in a time of casual grooming.

At the end of the day, or indeed upon any chance meeting, one or both cats would spontaneously provide their friend with the comfort such attentiveness brings.

Robert, being the younger, was grateful for the older cat's friendship, and grooming, for him, kindled recent memories of a maternal presence and the warm security of the litter.

Robert's innocent confession of his feelings to Oliver took the old cat by surprise, but he responded as well as he might.

"Kindness," said Oliver, "is as delicate as a floating bubble, but the remembrance of its beauty is a pillar of our being."

Moved by Oliver's tone and sincerity, Robert began to groom him, first behind the left ear and then behind the right, for, as is well known, cats cannot groom themselves in these places.

TO ALL APPEARANCES

Oliver, the old cat, was a very thoughtful cat. He often appeared to be sleeping when he was actually thinking, though some unkind creatures had suggested that he was a lazy cat.

Perhaps it was because Robert, the young cat, was so filled with the energy of youth that Oliver, by comparison, seemed torpid.

One day as Robert dashed here, and then there, and then here again, Hero, the kookaburra, who liked the garden to be an orderly place, decided to play a trick on Robert. Hero flew to the ground and pretended to be injured. He flapped about in such a way that it seemed he could not fly.

Robert stopped his dashing about and gave chase to Hero.

Hero managed to stay always just in advance of Robert's outstretched paws. Finally Robert made a great spring, but Hero flew up into the trees and from his perch he laughed a kookaburra's laugh.

Robert was crestfallen and complained to Oliver.

"Who is the greatest fool," said Oliver, "one who leads others into folly, or the one who follows the fool?"

"Your wise sayings do very little to cheer me up," chided Robert.

"A clever saying serves its purpose," replied Oliver, "if it makes its author appear clever."

And the old cat closed his eyes in what Robert imagined must be thoughtful repose.

WITH A HOLLER AND A WHOOP

ilda, the brush turkey, was an ungainly bird, but her legs were powerful and her wings adequate.

Robert, the young cat, had not yet learned to pretend that Hilda was not in the garden when, indeed, Hilda was in the garden.

Oliver, the old cat, had learned to pretend. He had chased Hilda, only to have her turn and scratch dirt into his eyes. Hilda had pressed home her advantage by pecking and chasing the confused cat.

Robert caught Hilda by surprise. When he gave chase she ran, and, with Robert at her tail feathers, she flapped clumsily into the treetops.

Robert laughed when Oliver told him of his experience. "An adventure is no adventure at all," he cried, "unless it begins with a holler and a whoop."

And in his dreams that afternoon as he lay in the crisp brown leaves under the bottlebrush tree, Oliver, racing at speed, had Hilda by the tail feathers.

FOR WHAT DOES IT PROFIT?

Angus, the carpet snake, was a lonely creature for he found it very difficult to find any other animal who would talk with him.

True, Angus ate most other forest animals, but he ate infrequently, and only when he was hungry.

One day Angus was very surprised when Hilda, the brush turkey, called to him from the trees above.

"Why did you steal my eggs?" croaked Hilda.

"You had left your mound, and I was hungry," said Angus.

"All brush turkeys leave their mounds, and the eggs are warmed by the leaves as they mould," rasped Hilda.

"Turkeys have chosen their way," said Angus. "Those who choose to neglect that which is most precious must be prepared to grieve for that which is lost."

And with that Angus slid off into the tangled green undergrowth.

THE IMPORTANCE OF BEING ROBERT

The forest beyond the garden was a wild place. The grunts and squeals of animals filled the night, and the screech of parrots startled those creatures who roamed by day.

The ebb and flow of the wind made the trees rustle as they bowed their heads, and the crack of fallen branches caused many an ear to prick.

Oliver, the old cat, had never travelled far into the forest. Once, beyond the garden fence, he had challenged a rat and been bitten. Oliver remembered the rat's bite and the sickness that followed.

Robert, the young cat, was fascinated by the forest and by what was beyond that which he could see. He explored by scampering to this tree and to that tree, retreating as quickly as he had come. Soon he began to recognise the places where he had been and was reassured by the familiar.

One day, thought Robert, I will have seen what is beyond every tree.

Angus, the carpet snake, watched Robert wander further and further away from the garden.

When Oliver spoke to Robert about the dangers of the forest, Robert listened carefully, but the very next day he went further into the forest than he had ever been before.

In his own way and in his own young life, Robert had already begun to understand that courage is measured by our victories over our greatest fears.

A Contented Cat

obert, the young cat, and Oliver, the old cat, were sitting, as they often did, on a high perch overlooking the garden.

"Why," said Robert (Robert's best and newest word was "why"), "why are humans so often sad?"

"They are sad," replied Oliver, "because they have forgotten how to be happy. Cats need only food for the day and leisure for dreaming. Humans are vexed unless their store is overflowing, and anxious when their hours are not filled."

"Why?" began Robert, but it was of no use, for Oliver had closed his eyes, and he was travelling in a familiar land where a quiet voice filled his mind with wisdom and his heart with content.

EACH NEW DAY

obert the young cat's favourite game was to run helter skelter down the path and climb the trunk of the eucalypt tree, scaling as high as his momentum would carry him.

His spirits were so high and his energy such that he often regretted that his enthusiasm had propelled him to a height from which it was difficult to climb down.

Flora, the frog-mouth owl, was convinced that one day Robert would reach her perch, so she sought advice from Oliver, the old cat.

Oliver said that he would think about the problem, and think about it he did.

The next day with a holler and a whoop, Robert charged the eucalypt. To his surprise he reached Flora's perch, whereupon the startled owl flapped upwards, and Robert fell headlong downwards. Robert survived and Flora recovered.

Oliver stopped thinking about Flora's problem because Robert promised never to run up the owl's tree again.

The next day, Robert ran up another tree.

Enthusiasm, concluded Oliver, is often an excuse for excess, but it is, after all, enthusiasm and not the desire for self preservation, which owns the world's new day.

LIFE THE TEACHER

obert, the young cat, was often restless. He found it very difficult to match the length of time which Oliver, the old cat, set aside for sleeping.

Robert would pace and leap and spar and feign, and, to be truthful, sometimes Oliver was quite glad when Robert went off by himself.

One day, as his restlessness grew, Robert exclaimed to Oliver, "I'm off to find an adventure!"

"Good," said Oliver, "and should you find one, and should you return, I'm sure I will be pleased to hear all about it."

As he set off, Robert was not sure that he was as keen on the idea of an adventure as he had been, but he did know that the excitement which he felt gave strength to his body and purpose to the moment.

As Robert left the safety of the garden his daring was tempered by natural caution. He began to tread warily, investigating every tree and shrub. Each step stirred a brew of uncertainty that trickled through his muscles before congealing in a hard lump below his breast bone.

Maxwell, the tom cat, waited patiently for Robert to peer under the

bush where he lay. The gnarled old tom was not a conversationalist. He believed in ferocity and was fluent in its monosyllabic language.

Maxwell reached the retreating Robert before he could scramble back over the garden fence and bit him about the tail and ears.

When he finally escaped, Robert skulked in the far reaches of the garden and rested until the evening, when he sought out Oliver.

"As I recall it," Oliver greeted Robert, "you were looking for an adventure, and from your appearance, I would say that one found you."

"I really do think," said Robert ruefully, "that you could have warned me about the risks I was taking."

"Aah, Robert lad," said Oliver, "it is the unknown which provides the risky winds by which an adventure sails. And very few there are, who are grateful to those who hoist foul weather signals at the journey's outset."

And, as Robert settled at his side, Oliver recalled his own adventures, and he numbered his scars. To live, he thought, is to be, and in being we learn as we sip at the fount from which wisdom drinks.

JUST PLAIN TREVOR

revor, the bearded dragon, lived in a dry hollow log in the garden and he ate the purple flowers which grew on the vine on the garden fence. Trevor's skin was rough, and it was the colour of the sky on a rainy day, lightened only by a pale sand mottle.

Trevor tried very hard not to upset anyone. When challenged he would stand still, so that, eventually, the creature making the challenge would simply lose interest.

Trevor's life was not one of highs and lows. He was neither optimistic nor pessimistic, and he had no desire to be green or brown. Trevor was pleased to be grey, because grey blends well with almost everything.

One day, Hilda, the brush turkey, pecked Trevor's tail, mistaking its thin, wiry shape for an insect.

Trevor quickly apologised to Hilda and was beside himself with concern lest he had upset her.

As it was, Hilda was too busy foraging to listen to Trevor, and she lacked the good manners to enquire about his tail.

Later, within his hollow log, Trevor tried very hard to understand why it is that mildness is seldom praised as a virtue. And he pondered, as he often did, upon why it should be that all creatures are not desirous of being grey, modestly overlaid with a pale sand mottle.

AT THE HEART OF THINGS

Flora, the frog-mouth owl, laid and hatched two eggs each year. She would glide with feathered softness through the night to seize in her claws small rodents which she would then bring to her insatiable chicks.

At the end of each season of nurture, Flora was exhausted.

Flora envied Hilda, the brush turkey for, once Hilda had laid her eggs and buried them in a mound of decaying leaves, she had no further cares. Hilda's chicks grubbed for themselves on the forest floor and Hilda had no further interest in them.

One day Hilda challenged Flora.

"Why is it," she gobbled, "that you waste your energies on your chicks? My brood is strong and independent, young things that are able to scratch for themselves and fend off their enemies with cunning."

Flora sighed. If only she could be as Hilda, her tired wings could take their ease. Then from her heart she made this reply.

"The most tender of my memories is the soft flutter of my mother's wings as she settled to the nest. If it should be that the sound of my wings is as dear to another, this would be my greatest joy."

"Owls," hissed Hilda, "must be free to be ill used, if that is their desire."

Flora, for her part, was content with an awakening within her, that the servant of self serves for self's sake, and the servant of love for love's sake.

AND WHAT ARE FRIENDS FOR?

His body motionless, his swivel eye angled, Trevor, the bearded dragon, met the stare of Robert, the young cat, who sat still in the rough grass – and they sat with stare fixed, and they sat with stare fixed.

From his high perch above the garden, Oliver, the old cat, watched.

Even the heat of the climbing sun could not persuade the lizard and the cat to break off the contest; but the warmth did cause Angus the carpet snake to stir . . . and he began to unwind his coils.

"Danger!" cried Oliver. Robert flinched. Trevor was away.

Robert was furious. He raced to Oliver's place of refuge, and in his anger bit the old cat about the hind legs.

Later, as Robert and Oliver sat together on the high perch recounting the day, Oliver tended his legs – but he was happy in his inner self, for his friend had been saved, and, for this, he could count his wounds as nothing.

Uniquely Me

 liver's hunting skills were those of an old cat. He was proud that he moved only as quickly and as much as he must to catch his prey.

Robert, the young cat, admired Oliver's swiftness and stealth, but it was not the way in which he hunted. For him, it was the charge and chase. Though he often missed his opportunities, it was never, to him, a cause for regret.

Hunting, for the young cat, had to do with energy and sport. After all, Robert didn't hunt because he was hungry; he hunted, because, well, cats hunt.

Oliver hunted mice. Robert leapt at grasshoppers and stood on the tails of skinks.

As Robert and Oliver nestled in the dry leaves under the bottlebrush tree, Robert asked his friend why it was that cats hunted.

"Hunting," replied Oliver, "keeps cats in touch with who they are. If I did not hunt, I would not be true to that which is me."

"If we fail to make a friend of what is special about us," said Oliver, "we begin to keep company with those whose steps leave no mark of their journey."

"For cats," he said, "hunting is a song which sings in our sinews, and it is part of the great song which sings in all things."

Robert folded his paws beneath him and let his chin rest upon his chest. The warmth and smell of the crisp and brown leaves suggested sleep. If hunting mice brought his friend to such seriousness, it was time, he thought, to dream of the marvellous sport to be had with grasshoppers.

CREATION'S PRAYER

Molly, the tree snake, was a shy, nervous creature, and she preferred to blend her lithe green body with the colour of the leaves and not be seen at all.

Each year Molly would shed her outer skin and the delicate lacy husk would eventually fall to the ground.

Robert, the young cat, knew that Molly lived in the trees for her discarded skin told him so . . . but Robert had never seen Molly.

Molly enjoyed watching Robert live out his young life in the garden. She smiled at his failures and admired his successes.

When Molly's eggs hatched in a secret place in the garden, the small snakes, one by one, fell prey to Robert.

Molly grieved a mother's grief, but she could not find it within herself to blame Robert for being what he was, a young cat.

Molly, from the safety of her leafy world, determined to overcome her fears and speak with Robert. She would have him understand that the fullness of the garden belonged to those who preserved its life, and the bitterness of its emptiness to those who despoiled it.

WATERLOO

obert! Robert! Robert! Robert! cried the accusing mickys. Mickys had discovered long ago that any likely predator could be driven off, even by birds as small as themselves, if they banded together in noisy protest. They spared no creature, with one accusing voice multiplying to a din and finally a crescendo.

Robert! Robert! Robert! piped the birds, as they chided the young cat, skulking beneath the bushes below. Beady eyes, made fierce by the fires of excitement, peered from under black caps, over sharp yellow beaks as in judgemental unison, they pointed, pointed, pointed to Robert! Robert! Robert!

Robert was not so much frightened by the birds, as embarrassed. Everyone, just everyone, enjoyed the joke of his frequent discovery and humiliation. Cats are supposed to be creatures of stealth, and Robert's pride was in tatters. If it was a game, it was a game which he had lost, lost, lost . . . and he was heartily sick of it.

Oliver, the old cat, noting his friend's despair, suggested that he would do well to stay out of the mickys' territory. Young creatures, however, neither take well to advice, nor are they known for their discretion.

The next moonless night, Robert stole silently into the birds'
domain, and climbed a tree in which the birds often gathered. As the
sun rose, he would be among the mickys before a cry could be raised.
He would have his revenge.

As Robert settled into a fork of the eucalypt to await the dawn,
he became momentarily aware of movement above him. Rhea, the
possum, her baby clinging to the fur of her back, snorted a cry of rage,
and she came at Robert with her teeth bared, and her sharp, terrible
claws scything the air before her.

As Oliver remarked later to his injured friend, the forest creatures
were defending only that which ensured their survival.

"Please, please, please spare me your sage remarks," begged Robert.
But Oliver did not.

"Each of us," said the old cat, "is entitled to protect what is fairly
held. Those who would take it away, may complain only of our resolve,
in their defeat, and boast of our lack of it, in their victory."

And Robert fell asleep, with his face upon his paws, and his tail
between his legs, and his friend at his side.

STANDING "TRUTH" ON ITS HEAD

Eric, the fruit bat, visited the garden on balmy summer evenings just as the light slipped from the sky. His black form could be seen in silent flight against the silver of twilight.

The paw paw tree in the garden belonged to Eric and no other and, with his cape of wings about him, he would hang upside down as he emptied the fruit of its ripe pulp.

Rhea, the ring tail possum, busy with her own food gathering, often passed nearby Eric as he gorged. Eric's manners were, as Rhea said, "nothing to write home about", but it was his peculiar habit of feeding upside down which aroused her curiosity.

Unable to refrain any longer from asking the question, Rhea enquired of Eric: "why don't you eat as other creatures eat? Why do you hang upside down?"

With the moonlight reflecting in his bright black eyes, Eric paused, and then answered, "what is upside down or right side up, depends largely upon one's position at the time." And with that, Eric shifted to where he could consume the next succulent fruit.

Later, as Rhea hung by her splendid tail to sip the nectar of the bloom of the tulip tree, she puzzled over Eric's answer.

What is upside down and right side up, she reasoned, is very much a personal view. She supposed, that if one's life is spent viewing things from down to up, it could just be that down becomes up and up becomes down. Perhaps, the one looking up may be right in the matter, and the many looking upside down, may be wrong. At least, Rhea concluded, as she swung upside down to reach further into the nectar cup, one shouldn't exclude the possibility.

A Time for Reflection

As Robert, the young cat, grew, Oliver, the old cat, began to take an increasing interest in Robert's behaviour and manners.

It was generally agreed in the garden, a word here and a word there, that Robert's devil-may-care attitude needed tempering; and there was a feeling about that he should be taken in hand.

Oliver realised, of course, that it would serve no purpose to approach the matter directly, for Robert was too glib and undisciplined to accept advice. The old cat closed his eyes and pondered until at last he came up with a scheme. Molly, the tree snake, who had attempted some previous conversation with Robert, admittedly from a high branch and certainly with little effect, was persuaded by Oliver to try to speak to Robert again.

"This time," said Oliver to Molly, "come further down the tree and speak more directly to the young cat."

"Remember," purred Oliver, "that he is likely to listen to your advice, for no other creature possesses the persuasiveness of your kind."

Molly summoned all her courage and called to Robert from a branch which almost stroked the ground.

When Robert saw Molly he ignored the invitation to conversation, and chased her up the eucalypt.

Molly slithered up the tree, higher and higher, and with great speed, until, her green skin blending with the leaves, she was lost in a confusion of colour.

Robert, when he came to his senses, and found that he was sitting in the highest fork of the eucalypt, began to mew.

After a time, Oliver called to Robert. "Robert," he crooned.

"Yes," replied Robert.

"What are you thinking?" enquired Oliver.

"I am thinking," said Robert, "that if I had been polite to Molly I wouldn't be up this tree."

"Perhaps you would like to think a little more, now that you have the time," said Oliver.

And before Oliver sought out a quiet place in the garden to consider at leisure a rescue plan for Robert, he reminded himself that good manners required that, sooner rather than later, he should apologise to Molly for any upset she may have suffered.

DARKNESS INTO LIGHT

Rhea, the ring tail possum, was a beautiful creature. Her coat was soft and thick, her tail long and tactile and her expression bright and enquiring. Rhea's head was surmounted by sharp, pricked ears, and her face was dominated by a pink nose and large lustrous eyes.

Possums are nocturnal, and they are infamous for the noise which they make, especially when they fight. The snort of a possum, and its grumbling growl, are as unlovely as the creature is lovely.

Night-time in the garden and its bordering forest was often filled with frightening sounds.

The thin wailing call of the curlew, and the sharp strident shriek of the plover, conjured up visions of unseen but terrible things as they echoed through the reaches of the bushland.

Darkness for Rhea, however, was a friend. She moved confidently through the night, caressed by its balmy warmth and comforted by the tender touch of a sudden breeze upon her whiskers. By the jig of moonlight or the waltz of blackness the possum travelled easily, for Rhea could see as if the night were day.

Just in advance of the heralds of dawn, Rhea would make her way home to her nest of twigs.

And it was on one such occasion that she encountered Hero, the kookaburra, as he stood ready to signal the rising of the sun.

"It will soon be day," said Hero, "and the light will drive away the darkness."

Without breaking her journey, Rhea replied, "Those who have eyes that see, need have no fear of the dark."

And the crackling laugh of the kookaburra awakened those asleep, and their eyes beheld the light.

Handsome and be Hanged

On most days, at most times, the garden was a tranquil place. True, the creatures of the garden hunted or avoided pursuers, but that was all part of a natural rhythm of existence. The rules were known and predictable results followed upon mistakes.

The seasons flowed with acceptable regularity, and each season was marked by the recurrence of familiar events. The only creatures who really disturbed the life of the garden were the humans who owned it. Their obsessive fussing and re-arranging made the garden's inhabitants cross.

Angus, the carpet snake, could be counted upon to shed his skin from nose to tail each time the fitting became too tight. In its newness, the skin was smooth and its pattern resplendent.

At these times, Angus liked to show off the pewter sheen of his skin and the lustre of his newborn colours, and he would coil and uncoil, or perhaps hang loosely from a tree.

Oliver, the old cat, who, from his high perch, took it upon himself to be the arbiter of what was acceptable to the garden's creatures, decided that Angus was acting above himself.

"It seems to have fallen to me," remarked Oliver to Angus, "to share with you the general view that your display could be construed by others as," and Oliver paused for effect, "as conceit."

"For myself," lisped Angus, "I would have put it rather differently. To be proud of one's appearance is a mark of gratitude; to invite others to admire one's appearance is conceit."

"Still," he continued, "if you see only offence in me, I will take myself off into the forest beyond the garden." And without further ado, he did.

Oliver settled comfortably on his high perch. It was satisfying to have the wisdom to judge another's fault, and, indeed, the presence of mind to point it out.

As the days passed and Angus did not return, Oliver became disquieted and less than pleased with himself. No longer could he look upon the handsomeness which followed the carpet snake's sheddings, and no longer could he catch his breath at the sight of a creature's splendour renewed.

Oliver was seized with regret. "To judge another," he sighed, "is a weighty matter, and those who take pleasure in it must accept as their reward, the certainty of their own perfection."

ABOVE HIMSELF

Hero, the kookaburra, laughed a kookaburra's laugh at first and last light. He alone seemed to know that exact moment, when morning's shards of light pierced the sky, or evening's needles of darkness blinded the sun.

Hero's world was ordered, and he liked to order the world – or at least, that part of the world which was the garden. Everything, for the kookaburra, followed in natural sequence, and he became cross when that pattern was disturbed. At day's end, he let it be known that the day was done, and at the coming of the morning he made sure that an audience was readied to gaze upon its fresh fairness.

Hero's insistence upon order made Robert, the young cat, cranky. "He bosses everything and everyone about," complained Robert. "He thinks he owns the garden," he whined to Oliver, the old cat.

"Hero's misfortune," ventured Oliver, "is to believe that one who chortles at dusk and dawn may command, as does the one who calls in the night and the day."

And Robert was pleased with Oliver's answer.

WHITE KNIGHTS

Trevor, the bearded dragon, could move quickly, but he usually moved slowly. His gait was awkward, and the peculiar jointing of his legs ensured that, even at the slowest pace, his body developed that rolling motion which is common to lizards large and small.

Whenever Trevor moved, he moved cautiously, stopping frequently to arch his body, whereupon his head and neck would become a periscope for eyes which would swivel to scan around and above.

A threat to no one, despite a show of pointed spines about his neck, the lizard was destined to undertake a lifetime of journeys, seized with the apprehension which belongs to the careful.

Robert, the young cat, held Trevor in disdain. The lizard had no fight in him, and as any hunter will tell you, the measure of the satisfaction of the blood lust is the degree to which the quarry resists its tormentor.

As a matter of balance, Oliver, the old cat, did not hide the fact that he had some sympathy for Trevor, and he said as much each time that Robert poured scorn upon the creature.

"Why do you take his side? You know that Trevor is frightened of his own shadow!" exclaimed an angry Robert.

But the older cat would not be moved. "Those who have known fear are they who must champion the fearful," he said.

And, for a time, the cats agreed that they would each keep to themselves their opinion of Trevor.

IN THE EYE OF THE BEHOLDER

Ezra, the cane toad, was aggrieved. He believed that he was discriminated against because he was a migrant and successful. All toads accept that other creatures find them less than handsome, but such a burden is not heavy when there are large numbers of your own kind to share it.

Cane toads had been taken from a far country and let loose to deliver the fields of sugar cane from a pestilent beetle. Obligingly, they had gone forth to consume heartily and multiply greatly. It seemed entirely reasonable, in the circumstances, that they should supplement their diet with the tadpoles and fingerlings of native frogs and fish. Ezra could only conclude that the scorn which this drew was based on ingratitude and resentment.

What made matters worse is that cane toads are sensitive creatures. The blop, blop, blop of Ezra's mating call may have been simply that to others, but to the toad, it was a love song, delivered with gentle nuance and warm passion.

One evening, after rain, Robert came upon Ezra, as the young cat sought out more certain shelter. Ill of sorts, because of his damp fur,

Robert cuffed Ezra, and the blow turned the toad over, exposing his yellow underside.

"Your belly is even more offensive than the rest of you," snarled Robert.

Righting himself, and puffing out his body to the fullest, Ezra flayed Robert with the lash of words: "You look outwards and see only ugliness, but my eyes reflect inwards to where the heart and beauty meet."

At that, Robert cuffed Ezra for a second time, turning him over once again.

As Robert moved off, shaking his wet paws, and seeking sympathy for his conviction that all cane toads deserve to be cuffed, Ezra picked himself up and, desiring consolation, hopped to his mating pad.

And into the blackness of the night the toad set free a lament from within: "Beauty commands its own audience, but the beauty of the soul struggles to find but one admirer."

ATTAINING THE HEIGHTS

"There he goes again!" exclaimed Robert, the young cat.

It was to be expected in the garden that there would be quiet times. All creatures require rest, not the least cats, and so natural pauses would arrive, to conveniently fill the gaps vacated by events.

Robert and Oliver, the old cat, often sought out a vantage point during these times, to rest, and to watch for any movement which would trigger their interest.

"I think he's going to try again," said Robert.

"Yes," nodded Oliver, "I think he is."

Settled comfortably, their paws beneath them and their heads upon their chests, the cats watched Raymond, the coucal, labour from tree to tree, as he sought to regain a high point. Having achieved his aim, Raymond would, once again, perform an uncertain glide back to whence he had come.

"I hesitate to be rude," remarked Oliver, "but Raymond appears to be a bird of three parts. He has the head of a crow, the tail of a pheasant and a middle that holds the ends together."

"I'm not sure," continued the old cat, "that he is even meant to fly."

45

R

"There he goes again!" cried Robert.

Moving only their eyes, the cats followed Raymond's dive, as, first he narrowly avoided the trees in his path, and then made a final scramble to break an alarming free fall.

"If it were not for his tail clasping at balls of air," observed Robert, "he would crash."

Oliver blinked his agreement.

"Do you think that a bird as ungainly as Raymond is, well, a mistake?" queried Oliver.

"I suppose," Robert replied, "that it rather depends upon whether you require perfection, and believe that you know what perfection is."

"There he goes again!" exclaimed Robert, but Oliver was suddenly preoccupied. To his surprise, he was playing host to a thought which had arrived with the unexpected message that his young friend was growing in wisdom.

Not So Much a Defeat

As Oliver, the old cat, grew even older, he began to give thought to the meaning of his life, and why it was that age had brought with it a slowing of his agility.

Oliver's life was bounded by the garden, for he seldom found anything of interest to him beyond it. If life had meaning, thought Oliver, it was, for him, centred upon the life which throbbed through the creatures which inhabited the garden. Oliver could see no other meaning outside the touchstones of reality represented by the day to day existence of the garden's community. Or could he? The question began to trouble him.

It was well known among all the creatures that Oliver was not the cat he used to be. His white whiskers alone told the birds that they could take liberties once undreamed of.

Cheeky butcher birds and jaunty mickys now stole crumbs where once that had been, at least, unwise.

One day, it was noticed that Oliver had vacated the watchtower, the high perch from which he had so long observed the life of the garden.

Perhaps he has become too old to care, thought the birds, as they made play on the vacant perch.

And so the birds, in mock parade, despoiled the old cat's retreat. Beguiled by their own bravado, and forgetful of the past, their surprise was complete when they became ever so briefly aware of a flashing black paw.

Age may have robbed me of my reflexes, thought Oliver, but its gift to me has been the gift of patience.

As Oliver settled again on his high perch, and began to groom the web of his paws, a growing confidence within reassured him that growing old is about adapting experience to circumstances.

And the meaning of life? Well, and he thought his deepest cat thoughts, perhaps that is about keeping safe the integrity of who we are, for the sake of what it is we hope to become.

AND IT WAS SO

The world, which was the garden, was inhabited by many creatures who used and divided it according to their strength, guile and needs. It provided sustenance and succour, and it was a cradle for the replenishment of life.

The late spring and early summer was a time of great activity. Plants increased and bloomed and their colours and nectars seduced passers-by with sugary potions. The cold-blooded creatures sought vantage points to charge their bodies with energy from the sun, and those with warm blood welcomed rays which caressed their muscle and sinew. The garden filled with the rustle, singing, calling, buzzing and slithering sounds of life, and those sounds added their music to the song of all created order.

Oliver, the old cat, took his solace and comfort from the rhythm of the garden. He knew that he could not control its life, for that was inexorable. His own experience had taught him that there was a height to his strength, and that his prime had passed. He had come to that moment of understanding wherein he knew that he had a part to play, but only for a time. The garden was there when he came to it, and it would be there when he went.

When the summer rains came, unleashed from distorted clouds gorged with moisture, and the season of thunder and lightning cowed the earth as it vandalised the sky, the garden provided the holes, hollows, logs and leaves of refuge. And all the while, the creatures of the garden completed those events of procreation which ensured another beginning.

As day succeeded day and seasons passed, Oliver, from his high perch, observed the garden and pondered its parade of beginnings and ends. As he grew older, that which had appeared to him to be a garment of rent pieces, now held out the promise that it was seamless.

Principal Players

Robert   **American shorthair**; classic red tabby. A young cat;
   confident, brash and adventurous.

Oliver   **British shorthair**; smoke (black), classic tabby. An old cat;
   conservative, introspective and loyal.

Hero   **blue-winged kookaburra** (*Dacelo Leachii*); medium size bird;
   strong beak; head off white, strongly streaked chocolate brown;
   wings, predominantly blue. Heard mainly at sun up or sun down;
   voice is a variation of the laughing kookaburra's "Koo, hoo-hoo-
   hoo-hoo-haha-ha-ha-ha-ha!"

Trevor   **bearded dragon** (*Pogona Barbata*); a large lizard; species vary
   in colour from pale grey to fawn or brown or almost black. Throat
   has well developed pouch or beard. A traverse series of enlarged
   spines which ring throat lends a prehistoric appearance.

Hilda   **brush turkey** (*Alectura*); a squat bird with strong legs; small
   turkey size; brownish black, head and neck bare with some red skin,
   fold of yellow around neck. No nonsense personality.

Angus   **carpet snake** (*Morelia Spilota*); large python, 2 to 4 m; capable
   of swallowing cats. Ranges in colour from pale to dark brown with
   blotches or variegations.

Flora   **tawny frog-mouth owl** (*Pod Argus Strigoides*); mouth is truly frog like. Plumage variable: streaked fawn, grey and dark grey. A hardy bird with a soulful appearance.

Molly   **tree snake** (*Dendrelaphis Punctulatus*); a slender, elegant tree dweller, 1 to 1.5 m. Many shades of green. Harmless.

Eric   **fruit bat** or **flying fox** (*Pteropus Alecto*); lives in large colonies, usually by water. Black fur over whole body, reddish collar. Head and body length 240 to 260 mm.

Rhea   **ring tail possum** (*Pseudocheirus Peregrinus*); rabbit-size marsupial; variable grey to almost black. Long white-tipped prehensile tail which tapers to a slender tip.

Ezra   **cane toad** (*Bufo Marinus*); South American toad imported into Australia. Large; brownish topside with yellowish underside. Poison glands at neck. Almost universally disliked by people of Queensland, who hold cane toad hunts with the object of eliminating the species.

Raymond   **pheasant coucal** (*Centropus Phasianinus*); large, long tailed, clumsy, curious-looking bird. Mainly black with reddish brown underparts. Bronze wings with black bar.

Maxwell   A cunning old tom cat.

Minor Players

Micky or **noisy miner** (*Manorina Melanoce Phala*); small bird which bands together in numbers to see off predators. Pale grey, white face and forehead; black crown and cheeks; grey rump and yellow bill. Bright personality.

Grey butcherbird (*Cracticus Torquatus*); medium size, stout bill; black face, white lores; white collar joined to white underparts; bluish grey back; tail, black, broadly tipped with white. Cocky and fearless.

Masked plover or **lapwing** (*Vanellus Miles*); size intermediate. Thin black stripe on hind neck and arrow black patch on shoulder and side of breast; facial wattle. Grey back; wing spurs, yellow with black tip. Voice: loud "Keer-kick-ki-ki-ki" and other strident notes. Night cries are startling.

Bush curlew (*Burhinus Magnirostris*); larger bird. Grey; white shoulder patch, streaked upper parts and breast. Sullen personality. Voice: loud, mournful "Wee-loo" or "Ker-loo" – usually heard at night and at a distance.

Dedication

In July of 1991, when my friend Brian Walsh visited my wife Joan and me in Brisbane, it was apparent that he was not well. His usual irrepressible energy was missing, and it became obvious that he was reviewing his life rather than impatiently pursuing the next frenetic moment.

Later that year, he was diagnosed as having lymphoma, that is, cancer of the lymph glands, the body's natural defence system.

With the same determination with which he faced all of life's problems, Brian submitted himself to chemotherapy, and he committed himself absolutely to recovery. "I would never pray, 'Heal me please!' I would pray, 'Help me to co-operate with you in your will to heal me, and with all those who are co-operating with you.'" His prayer to God revealed the strength of his personal faith.

Throughout this period Brian looked forward to receiving messages from his friends. He called it "contact ministry."

Brian had a cat called Thumper, and Thumper meant a great deal to him.

Somehow, because of Brian's love for Thumper, the Robert and Oliver stories began to form a part of the messages which filled the cards that I sent to him.

The stories were not message sticks for Brian, they were simply stories which reflected life; a means of enabling one friend to speak to the other about things usually left unsaid.

Sadly, by the beginning of 1993, despite earlier hopes of a reprieve, Brian was informed by his doctors that he had only a few months to live. He lived out those months with flair and great courage. He gave absolute witness to his Christian faith.

From the desire, therefore, of one human being to communicate concern and affection to another, arose the misadventures of Robert, and the reflections of Oliver.

From within there is, perhaps, a message for us all.

Brian died on July 15th, 1993.

This book is dedicated to my friend Brian Lawrence Walsh.